No Nonsense
Maths

8-9 years

Central pull-out pages

Parents' notes   A1
Answers   A2-4

Contents

www.bondlearning.co.uk

Thousands, hundreds, tens and units

THOUSANDS	HUNDREDS	TENS	UNITS
3	4	2	6

Three thousand, four hundred and twenty-six

1. **Match the written number with the correct card. Join the dots.**

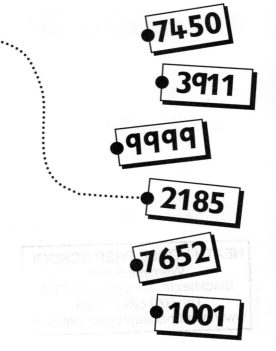

   a Two thousand, one hundred and eighty-five •

   b Seven thousand, four hundred and fifty •

   c One thousand and one •

   d Three thousand, nine hundred and eleven •

   e Seven thousand, six hundred and fifty-two •

   f Nine thousand, nine hundred and ninety-nine •

   7450
   3911
   9999
   2185
   7652
   1001

2. **What number needs to go in the gap?**

   a 3721 = __3000__ + 700 + 20 + 1

   b 4693 = 4000 + _____ + 90 + 3

   c 1978 = 1000 + 900 + _____ + 8

   d 5065 = 5000 + 0 + 60 + _____

   e 2860 = _____ + 800 + 60 + 0

   f 7602 = 7000 + 600 + 0 + _____

3. **Write these numbers as words.**

a 1276 _____

b 5628 _____

c 4600 _____

d 2890 _____

4. **Put these numbers in order, smallest first.**

3218   1796   3812   1976

_____   _____   _____   _____

5. **Which is more?**

a 1278 or 7281 _____   b 5820 or 5280 _____

c 3859 or 3985 _____   d 3796 or 4796 _____

e 9671 or 9617 _____   f 7772 or 7771 _____

Tough	OK	Got it!

0   21

Total

/

21

More practice? Go to www

Challenge yourself

Use all these digits.   2 7 9 3

a   Make the smallest number you can. _____

b   Make the biggest number you can. _____

c   Now write 2793 in words.

_____

3

Addition

When adding large numbers it is easier to lay them out like this.

$$127$$
$$+ \ 35$$
$$\overline{\ \ ?\ \ }$$

Look carefully at how we do this addition.

$$127$$
$$+ \ 35$$
$$\overline{\ \ 2\ \ }$$
$$\scriptstyle 1$$

First add the units together.
7 + 5 = 12

Write the units in the units column and 'carry' the ten into the tens column.

Next, add together the tens:
2 + 3 = 5 **BUT**

$$127$$
$$+ \ 35$$
$$\overline{\ 62\ }$$
$$\scriptstyle 1$$

don't forget to add the ten you 'carried' from the units.
2 + 3 + 1 = 6

Then add the hundreds:
1 + 0 = 1

$$127$$
$$+ \ 35$$
$$\overline{162}$$
$$\scriptstyle 1$$

Write the answer in the hundreds column.
So **127 + 35 = 162**

QUICK TIP!
Remember to put the units in the units column.

1. **Find the answers.**

a
$$\begin{array}{r} 126 \\ + \ \ 45 \\ \hline \\ \hline \end{array}$$

b
$$\begin{array}{r} 257 \\ + \ \ 24 \\ \hline \\ \hline \end{array}$$

c
$$\begin{array}{r} 218 \\ + \ \ 78 \\ \hline \\ \hline \end{array}$$

d	326 + 135	e	237 + 145	f	169 + 222
	_____		_____		_____

2. Complete each addition.

a	173 +118	b	261 +119	c	327 +125
	2 1		80		45
	_____		_____		_____

d	215 + 57	e	159 +186	f	261 +149
	72		34		1
	_____		_____		_____

0				12
	Tough	OK	Got it!	

Total

12

More practice? Go to www

Challenge yourself

Using two of these numbers, write as many different additions as you can. Then write the answers.

25   68   17   42   79

```
   2 5
+ 4 2
─────
   6 7
─────
```

Check your answers on a calculator.

5

Subtraction

To subtract larger numbers it is easier to write them like this.

```
   73
 – 48
 ────
    ?
 ────
```

Look carefully at how to do this ...

```
   73              70 + 3
 – 48      =   –   40 + 8
 ────              ──────
```

First take away the units BUT you cannot take 8 away from 3.

```
   73              60 + 13
 – 48          –   40 +  8
 ────              ───────
    5                    5
 ────
```

So change one ten into units. This leaves 6 tens and 13 units. Now you can take 8 away from 13.

```
   73              60 + 13
 – 48          –   40 +  8
 ────              ───────
   25              20 +  5  = 25
 ────
```

Then take away the tens.

So **73 – 48 = 25**

1. **Complete these subtractions.**

a
```
   5 6
 − 2 7
 ─────

 ─────
```

b
```
   7 3
 − 1 6
 ─────

 ─────
```

c
```
   6 5
 − 3 7
 ─────

 ─────
```

d
```
   8 3
 − 1 7
 ─────

 ─────
```

e
```
   4 2
 − 3 3
 ─────

 ─────
```

f
```
   5 6
 − 3 9
 ─────

 ─────
```

g
```
   6 3
 − 3 8
 ─────

 ─────
```

h
```
   5 6
 − 2 9
 ─────

 ─────
```

| 0 | Tough | OK | Got it! | 8 |

Total

8

More practice? Go to

Challenge yourself

Choose two 2-digit numbers. _____ _____

Now subtract each number from 162.

```
  162              162
−                −
─────            ─────

─────            ─────
```

3 and 4 times tables

Do you remember?

$8 \times 3 = 24$

$5 \times 4 = 20$

1. **Multiply these numbers.**

$1 \times 3 = \rule{2cm}{0.4pt}$　　　　　$1 \times 4 = \rule{2cm}{0.4pt}$

$2 \times 3 = \rule{2cm}{0.4pt}$　　　　　$2 \times 4 = \rule{2cm}{0.4pt}$

$3 \times 3 = \rule{2cm}{0.4pt}$　　　　　$3 \times 4 = \rule{2cm}{0.4pt}$

$4 \times 3 = \rule{2cm}{0.4pt}$　　　　　$4 \times 4 = \rule{2cm}{0.4pt}$

$5 \times 3 = \rule{2cm}{0.4pt}$　　　　　$5 \times 4 = \rule{2cm}{0.4pt}$

$6 \times 3 = \rule{2cm}{0.4pt}$　　　　　$6 \times 4 = \rule{2cm}{0.4pt}$

$7 \times 3 = \rule{2cm}{0.4pt}$　　　　　$7 \times 4 = \rule{2cm}{0.4pt}$

$8 \times 3 = \rule{2cm}{0.4pt}$　　　　　$8 \times 4 = \rule{2cm}{0.4pt}$

$9 \times 3 = \rule{2cm}{0.4pt}$　　　　　$9 \times 4 = \rule{2cm}{0.4pt}$

$10 \times 3 = \rule{2cm}{0.4pt}$　　　　　$10 \times 4 = \rule{2cm}{0.4pt}$

2. **Finish the times tables number sequences.**

a		15		24			

b	20			36			

3. **Answer these questions.**

   a What are three fours? _____

   b What is 10 times 4? _____

   c What is 3 multiplied by 8? _____

   d What are seven threes? _____

   e Multiply nine by four. _____

   f What is 4 multiplied by 6? _____

4. **Answer these as quickly as possible.**

   a $3 \times 3 =$ _____   b $8 \times 4 =$ _____

   c $7 \times 3 =$ _____   d $10 \times 3 =$ _____

   e $4 \times 4 =$ _____   f $2 \times 4 =$ _____

   g $9 \times 3 =$ _____   h $9 \times 4 =$ _____

0   Tough   OK   Got it!   17

Total 17

More practice? Go to www

Challenge yourself

Fill in the gaps.

a $5 \times$ _____ $= 15$ b $8 \times$ _____ $= 24$

c _____ $\times 4 = 24$ d _____ $\times 4 = 36$

e $1 \times$ _____ $= 4$ f _____ $\times 3 = 27$

g _____ $\times 3 = 24$ h _____ $\times 4 = 40$

i $4 \times$ _____ $= 16$ j $7 \times$ _____ $= 21$

Division facts

Division means you **share something equally**.
We share 12 cakes equally between Jack, Todd and Kathy.

They have 4 cakes each. **12 ÷ 3 = 4**

When dividing, it really helps if you know your times tables.
Look at how they can help you.

12 ÷ 3 = 4   12 = 3 x 4

1.   Fill in the gaps.

    a 10 ÷ 5 = 2   10 = 5 × __2__

    b 8 ÷ 2 = 4   8 = 2 × _____

    c 15 ÷ 5 = 3   15 = 5 × _____

    d 4 ÷ 1 = 4   4 = 1 × _____

    e 16 ÷ 4 = 4   16 = _____ × _____

    f 20 ÷ 5 = 4   20 = _____ × _____

    g 30 ÷ 6 = 5   30 = _____ × _____

    h 30 ÷ 3 = 10   _____ = _____ × _____

2. **Use multiplication facts to find the answers.**

a $45 \div 9 =$ _____ $\qquad$ $45 = 9 \times 5$

b $24 \div 6 =$ _____ $\qquad$ $24 = 6 \times 4$

c $80 \div 10 =$ _____ $\qquad$ $80 = 10 \times 8$

d $70 \div 10 =$ _____ $\qquad$ $70 = 10 \times$ _____

e $40 \div 5 =$ _____ $\qquad$ $40 = 5 \times$ _____

f $30 \div 6 =$ _____ $\qquad$ $30 = 6 \times$ _____

3. **Write the answers as quickly as possible.**

a Share 16 equally between 4. _____ $\qquad$ **b** How many fives are in 25? _____

c Divide 45 by 5. _____ $\qquad$ **d** Share 90 equally between 10. _____

e How many sixes in 18? _____ $\qquad$ **f** Divide 20 by 2. _____

Tough	OK	Got it!	19

0

Total

19

More practice? Go to www

Challenge yourself

Solve these problems.

a Rupesh has to buy 25 cakes for his gran.

There are 5 cakes in a box.

How many boxes will he need to buy? _____

b Annie had to buy 50 cakes for her dad's birthday party.

There are 5 cakes in a box.

How many boxes did she buy? _____

11

Multiplying and dividing by 10

When you multiply a number by 10 the digits move one place to the left.

$3 \times 1 = 3$

$3 \times 10 = 30$

1. **Multiply these single digit numbers by 10.**

a $1 \times 10 = $ _____

b $2 \times 10 = $ _____

c $3 \times 10 = $ _____

d $4 \times 10 = $ _____

e $5 \times 10 = $ _____

f $6 \times 10 = $ _____

2. **Now multiply these numbers by 10.**

a $26 \times 10 = $ _260_

b $37 \times 10 = $ _____

c $58 \times 10 = $ _____

d $96 \times 10 = $ _____

e $121 \times 10 = $ _____

f $113 \times 10 = $ _____

Look what happens when we keep multiplying a number by 10.
What do you notice?

$42 \times 10 = 420$

$420 \times 10 = 4200$

$4200 \times 10 = 42000$

3. **Try these.**

$86 \times 10 = $ _860_

$29 \times 10 = $ _290_

$860 \times 10 = $ _____

$290 \times 10 = $ _____

$8600 \times 10 = $ _____

$2900 \times 10 = $ _____

4. **Now look what happens when you divide by 10.**

a 10 ÷ 10 = _____

b 40 ÷ 10 = _____

c 20 ÷ 10 = _____

d 50 ÷ 10 = _____

e 30 ÷ 10 = _____

f 60 ÷ 10 = _____

When you divide a number by 10 the digits move one place to the right.

30 ÷ 1 = 30
30 ÷ 10 = **3**

---

5. **Divide these numbers by 10.**

a 60 ÷ 10 = __6__

b 80 ÷ 10 = _____

c 120 ÷ 10 = _____

d 170 ÷ 10 = _____

e 150 ÷ 10 = _____

f 190 ÷ 10 = _____

g 220 ÷ 10 = _____

h 360 ÷ 10 = _____

0   Tough   OK   Got it!   28

Total

28

More practice? Go to www

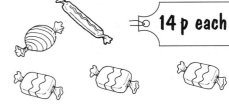

14 p each

Challenge yourself

Answer these questions.

a You buy 10 sweets and they cost 14p each.
How much will they all cost? _____

b There are 10 tins of dog food in a pack that cost £4.20 (420p).
How much would 1 tin cost? _____

c Parklands School has 260 children. There are 10 classes.
There are the same number of children in each class.
How many children is that? _____

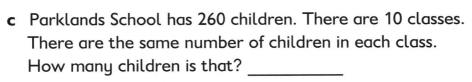

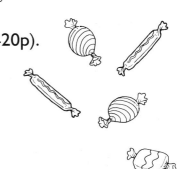

Fractions

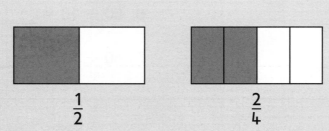

The same shaded fraction can be written in different ways.

The fraction $\frac{1}{2}$ is the same as $\frac{2}{4}$.

These are called **equivalent fractions**.

1. **Colour the fractions and fill in the gaps.**

a

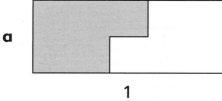

$\frac{1}{2}$ is the same as $\frac{5}{10}$

b

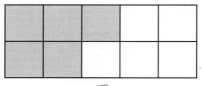

$\frac{1}{4}$ is the same as   _____

c

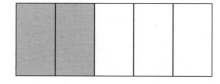

$\frac{2}{5}$ is the same as   _____

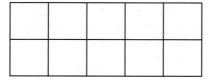

d

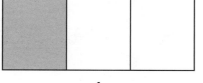

$\frac{1}{3}$ is the same as   _____

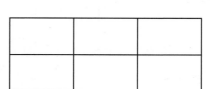

2. Circle the fractions that are bigger than $\frac{1}{2}$.

$\frac{3}{4}$ $\frac{2}{5}$ $\frac{1}{3}$ $\frac{2}{3}$ $\frac{7}{8}$ $\frac{6}{10}$

1 whole equals…

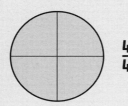 $\frac{4}{4}$

…when a circle is split into quarters.

3. Finish the fractions.

a $1 = \dfrac{}{2}$ **b** $1 = \dfrac{}{10}$ **c**  $1 = \dfrac{}{3}$

4. Finish these number sentences.

a $\frac{1}{4} + \frac{3}{4} = 1$ **b** $\frac{1}{3} + \dfrac{}{3} = 1$ **c** $\frac{1}{5} + \dfrac{}{5} = 1$

0			9
Tough	OK	Got it!	

Total

More practice? Go to www

Challenge yourself

Join pairs of equivalent fractions with a line.

 $\frac{1}{5}$ $\frac{4}{6}$ $\frac{2}{10}$ $\frac{4}{8}$ $\frac{7}{7}$

 $\frac{2}{2}$ $\frac{2}{3}$ $\frac{1}{2}$ $\frac{3}{4}$  $\frac{6}{8}$

15

Money

We are going to add and subtract amounts of money.

You have to remember to **keep the decimal point in line** when writing out the calculations – like this:

$$
\begin{array}{r}
£1\cdot24 \\
+\ £2\cdot12 \\
\hline
£3\cdot36 \\
\hline
\end{array}
\qquad
\begin{array}{r}
£4\cdot27 \\
£1\cdot16 \\
\hline
£3\cdot11 \\
\hline
\end{array}
$$

> **QUICK TIP!**
> Lessons 2 and 3 will remind you how to add and subtract if you have forgotten!

1. **Work out the answers.**

a
$$
\begin{array}{r}
£2\cdot31 \\
+\ £1\cdot56 \\
\hline
£ \\
\hline
\end{array}
$$

b
$$
\begin{array}{r}
39\,p \\
-\ 26\,p \\
\hline
p \\
\hline
\end{array}
$$

c
$$
\begin{array}{r}
£1\cdot30 \\
+\ £1\cdot69 \\
\hline
£ \\
\hline
\end{array}
$$

d
$$
\begin{array}{r}
£1\cdot38 \\
-\ \ \ 29\,p \\
\hline
£ \\
\hline
\end{array}
$$

e
$$
\begin{array}{r}
£3\cdot66 \\
+\ £2\cdot56 \\
\hline
£ \\
\hline
\end{array}
$$

f
$$
\begin{array}{r}
£2\cdot56 \\
-\ £1\cdot37 \\
\hline
£ \\
\hline
\end{array}
$$

g
$$
\begin{array}{r}
£3\cdot84 \\
+\ £4\cdot37 \\
\hline
£ \\
\hline
\end{array}
$$

h
$$
\begin{array}{r}
£2\cdot34 \\
-\ £1\cdot67 \\
\hline
£ \\
\hline
\end{array}
$$

i
$$
\begin{array}{r}
£3\cdot92 \\
+\ £5\cdot76 \\
\hline
£ \\
\hline
\end{array}
$$

2. How many pence?

a £2·78 = ___278p___

b £5·20 = _____

c £10·88 = _____

d £28·09 = _____

3. Write in pounds.

a 632p = ___£6·32___

b 250p = _____

c 893p = _____

d 3164p = _____

4. For his party Rashid spent ...

£1·20 on crisps

£4·74 on a cake

£1·85 on balloons

a Can he pay for all of this with £10.00? _____

b How much does it cost him? _____

c How much change does he get? _____

Tough	OK	Got it!	

0   18

Total

18

More practice? Go to

Challenge yourself

Solve these problems. Show your workings.

a James has £1. He buys five pens at 16p each.
How much change does he get? _____

b Gemma buys three scarves at £4·78 each.
What was her change from £20? _____

c Brian has two 50p coins and two 20p coins.
He spends 90p to ride a donkey on the beach.
How much money does he have left? _____

Time – analogue and digital

A clock with hands is called an **analogue** clock.

A clock with only numbers is called a **digital** clock.

HOUR   MINUTES

2:35

A digital clock clearly shows the number of minutes past the hour.

1. **Fill in the digital clocks.**

a

b

c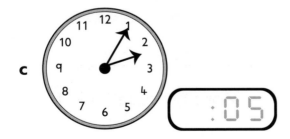

d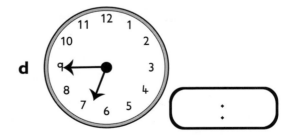

e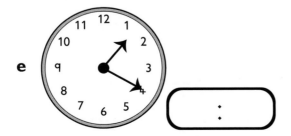

f

2. **Look at the digital clocks. Draw the correct time on the analogue clock.**

a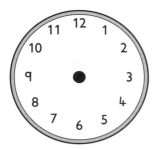

b

c

d

e

f

0			11
Tough	OK	Got it!	

Total

More practice? Go to www

Challenge yourself

How many?

a 1 minute = _____ seconds

b 1 hour = _____ minutes

c 1 day = _____ hours

d 1 week = _____ days

e 1 year = _____ weeks

f 1 century = _____ years

Co-ordinates

Co-ordinates give an **exact** place on a grid.

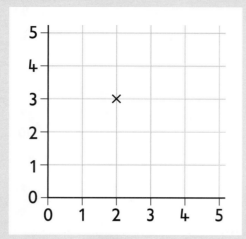

QUICK TIP!
Remember, you **always** go across first.

The point marked X has the co-ordinates (2, 3).

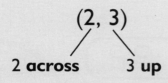

(2, 3)

2 **across**   3 **up**

1. **Look at these grids and write the co-ordinates for point X.**

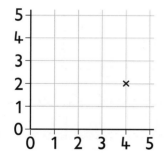

a (_____ , _____)

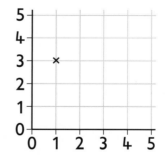
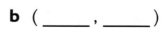

b (_____ , _____)

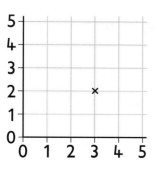

c (_____ , _____)

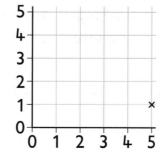

d (_____ , _____)

2. You can have more than one set of co-ordinates on a grid. Place neat crosses on this grid for the co-ordinates listed. The first two have been done for you.

(2 , 5)

(5 , 7)

(8 , 6)

(10 , 8)

(10 , 2)

(8 , 4)

(5 , 3)

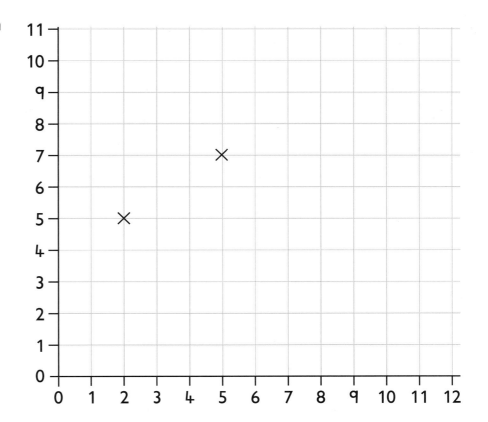

Neatly join the crosses in the same order.

What have you drawn? _____

0			5
Tough	OK	Got it!	

Total

More practice? Go to www

Challenge yourself

Choose a point anywhere on the grid at the top of page 20. Make a note of its co-ordinates on a separate piece of paper.

Now ask other people to put a cross where your point might be. Write down their co-ordinates.

(___ , ___) (___ , ___) (___ , ___) (___ , ___) (___ , ___)

Did anyone guess correctly? _____

How many guesses did it take? _____

1. **Put these numbers in order, smallest first.**

2238   1796   2138   3926

_____   _____   _____   _____

2. **Work out the answers.**

a   128
    + 54
    _____

    _____

b   134
    + 27
    _____

    _____

c   213
    + 48
    _____

    _____

d   184
    + 19
    _____

    _____

3. **Work out the answers.**

a   74
    − 26
    _____

    _____

b   56
    − 27
    _____

    _____

c   62
    − 34
    _____

    _____

d   81
    − 49
    _____

    _____

4. **Do these as quickly as you can.**

a $4 \times 3 =$ _____

b $9 \times 4 =$ _____

c $8 \times 3 =$ _____

d $10 \times 3 =$ _____

e $6 \times 4 =$ _____

f $3 \times 3 =$ _____

5. **Fill the gaps.**

a $9 \div 3 =$ _____

$9 = 3 \times$ _____

b $12 \div 4 =$ _____

$12 = 4 \times$ _____

c $16 \div 8 =$ _____

$16 = 8 \times$ _____

d $20 \div 4 =$ _____

$20 = 4 \times$ _____

6. **a** $21 \times 10 =$ _____ **b** $360 \div 10 =$ _____

   c $39 \times 10 =$ _____ **d** $110 \div 10 =$ _____

   e $55 \times 10 =$ _____ **f** $280 \div 10 =$ _____

7. **Complete these number sentences.**

   a $\frac{3}{4} + \frac{1}{4} =$ _____ **b** $\frac{1}{3} + \frac{}{3} = 1$

   c $\frac{5}{10} + \frac{}{10} = 1$ **d** $\frac{2}{5} + \frac{}{5} = 1$

8. **Write these in pounds.**

   a 451p = _____ **b** 230p = _____

   c 773p = _____ **d** 806p = _____

9. **Fill in the digital clocks.**

   a  **b**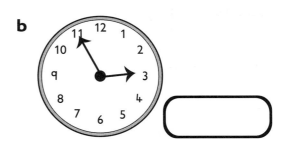

10. **Mark these co-ordinates on the grid.**

   a (1, 5) **b** (4, 3)

Total

37

More practice? Go to www

Greater than, less than

These numbers are in order from smallest to largest.

861   1435   2345   3305   4461   5173   6500

1. **Answer these questions.**

   a Which number is the smaller? 4589 or 4582 _____

   b Which number is the larger? 1197 or 1187 _____

   c Which measurement is the longer? 367 m or 421 m _____

   d Which measurement is the shorter? 1116 m or 1019 m _____

   e Which weight is the lighter? 863 g or 1211 g _____

   f Which weight is the heavier? 5218 kg or 5182 kg _____

2. **Put these numbers in order, largest first.**

   a 3671   6371   7361   1367   1763

      _____   _____   _____   _____   _____

   b 5534   5345   3455   5435   4553

      _____   _____   _____   _____   _____

   c 1298   1928   9281   8129   8921

      _____   _____   _____   _____   _____

3. **Add a number to each gap so the numbers go up from smallest to largest.**

   a 3480   _____   3790   _____   4100

   b 7845   _____   7850   _____   7855

c 1287 _____ 1290 _____ 1293

d 4444 _____ 5555 _____ 6666

The signs > and < are a quick way of writing '**more than**' and '**less than**'.

45 > 23 means 45 **is more than** 23
23 < 45 means 23 **is less than** 45

QUICK TIP!
The point of the sign is always next to the smaller number!

4. **Put the correct sign in the box.**

a 75 ☐ 94

b 43 ☐ 41

c 83 ☐ 49

d 67 ☐ 76

e 136 ☐ 163

f 743 ☐ 437

g 386 ☐ 368

h 791 ☐ 761

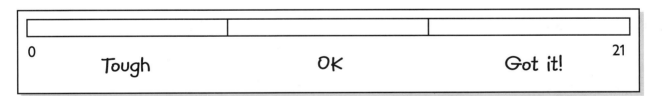

0   Tough   OK   Got it!   21

Total
21

More practice? Go to

Challenge yourself

Add a number to make each statement correct.

a 470 < _____

b 699 > _____

c 3280 > _____ > 1450

d 458 < _____ < 500

e 532 > _____ > 500

f 7320 < _____ > 7333

Negative numbers

We use **positive** numbers most of the time.

5 6 7 8 9

Sometimes we need to use **negative** numbers.

−5 −6 −7 −8 −9

We know it is a **negative number** because it has a − sign in front of it.

We use negative numbers when we measure cold temperatures with a thermometer.

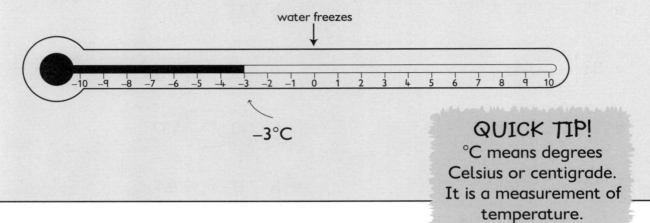

water freezes

−3°C

> **QUICK TIP!**
> °C means degrees
> Celsius or centigrade.
> It is a measurement of
> temperature.

1. **Carefully read the temperatures on the thermometers.**

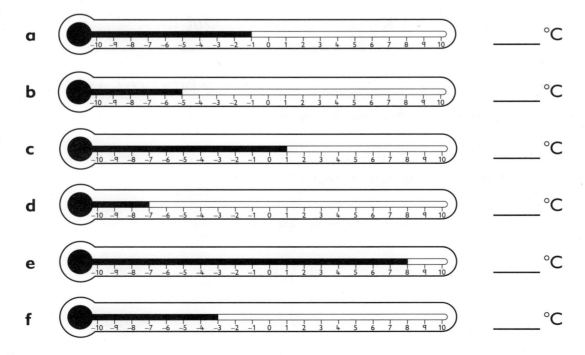

a   _____ °C

b   _____ °C

c   _____ °C

d   _____ °C

e   _____ °C

f   _____ °C

2. Estimate what number is marked with an arrow on these number lines.

a −10   0   10

Estimation _____

b −10   0   10

Estimation _____

c −10   0   10

Estimation _____

d −10   0   10

Estimation _____

e −10   0   10

Estimation _____

f −10   0   10

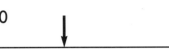

Estimation _____

3. Fill in the gaps.

−11		−9			−6		−4			−1	0		2	3		5

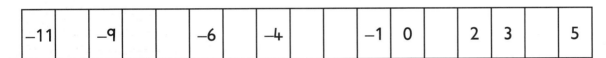

0			13
Tough	OK	Got it!	

Total

/ 13

More practice? Go to **www**

More practice? Go to www

Challenge yourself

Mark with an arrow and label the numbers below on the number line.

  −2   **5**   **−7**   **8**   **−1**   **−9**

(−2)

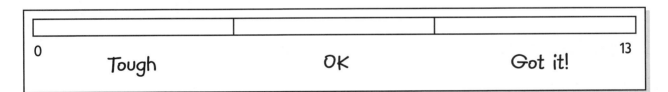

−10   0   10

Number sequences

Look at these number lines.
The numbers go **up 3** at a time.

53	56	59	62	65	68	71	74	77	80	83	86

The numbers go **down 5** at a time.

99	94	89	84	79	74	69	64	59	54	49	44

1. **Look for the pattern.**
   Finish the number sequences and complete the sentences.

   a
18	22	26	30	34	38	42	46	50	54	58	62

   The numbers go ___up___ ___4___ at a time.

   b
60	55	50	45	40	35	30	25				

   The numbers go _____ _____ at a time.

   c
46	44	42	40	38	36	34	32				

   The numbers go _____ _____ at a time.

   d
43	40	37	34	31	28	25	22				

   The numbers go _____ _____ at a time.

2. Fill in the missing numbers.

a

17	22		32	37	42			57	62		72

b

93	91	89		85		81		77		73	71

c

18	22		30	34		42	46		54	58	

d

72	69	66		60	57				45	42	39

3. Fill in the missing numbers but watch out ... these number sequences include negative numbers!

a

18	16	14		10	8		4	2	0		−4

b

−10	−7		−1	2		8	11		17	20	

c

	40	35	30	25			10	5		−5	−10

d

−9		−1		7	11	15	19	23		31	

0			11
	Tough	OK	Got it!

Total

11

More practice? Go to www

Challenge yourself

Colour the multiples of 4.

Look carefully at the pattern. What do you notice?

_____

If the pattern continued, would you colour the following numbers?

44 _____

53 _____

1	2	3	4	5	6
7	8	9	10	11	12
13	14	15	16	17	18
19	20	21	22	23	24
25	26	27	28	29	30
31	32	33	34	35	36

Multiplication 1

$15 \times 7 = ?$

When we multiply large numbers it is easier to lay them out like this.

```
  15
× 7
―――
  ?
―――
```

15×7 is the same as **$(10 + 5) \times 7 = (10 \times 7) + (5 \times 7)$**

```
  10            5
× 7           × 7
――――         ――――
  70    +      35
――――         ――――
```

```
  15
× 7
――――
  70      (10 × 7)
+ 35      ( 5 × 7)
――――
 105      (15 × 7)        15 × 7 = 105
――――
```

Here is another multiplication:

```
  12
× 8
――――
  80      (10 × 8)
+ 16      ( 2 × 8)
――――
  96      (12 × 8)
――――
```

1. **Fill in the gaps. Complete each multiplication.**

a
```
     14
×     6
――――――――
        (10 × 6)
――――    ( 4 × 6)
   8 4  (14 × 6)
――――――――
```

b
```
     19
×     5
――――――――
        (10 × 5)
――――    ( 9 × 5)
   9 5  (19 × 5)
――――――――
```

c
```
     21
×     3
――――――――
        (20 × 3)
――――    ( 1 × 3)
   6 3  (21 × 3)
――――――――
```

d
$$\begin{array}{r} 15 \\ \times\ \ 6 \\ \hline \end{array}$$
(10 × 6)

(5 × 6)

(15 × 6)

e
$$\begin{array}{r} 23 \\ \times\ \ 2 \\ \hline \end{array}$$
(20 × 2)

(3 × 2)

(23 × 2)

f
$$\begin{array}{r} 14 \\ \times\ \ 4 \\ \hline \end{array}$$
(10 × 4)

(4 × 4)

(14 × 4)

2. **Multiply these numbers.**

a
$$\begin{array}{r} 19 \\ \times\ \ 5 \\ \hline \end{array}$$

b
$$\begin{array}{r} 13 \\ \times\ \ 2 \\ \hline \end{array}$$

c
$$\begin{array}{r} 17 \\ \times\ \ 3 \\ \hline \end{array}$$

d
$$\begin{array}{r} 11 \\ \times\ \ 9 \\ \hline \end{array}$$

e
$$\begin{array}{r} 15 \\ \times\ \ 8 \\ \hline \end{array}$$

f
$$\begin{array}{r} 16 \\ \times\ \ 5 \\ \hline \end{array}$$

0			12
Tough	OK	Got it!	

Total

12

More practice? Go to

Challenge yourself

In Haughton village school there were 5 classes.
In each class there were 15 boys and 14 girls.

a How many boys went to the school? _____

b How many girls went to the school? _____

c How many children went to the school? _____

Division

We can write a division calculation in different ways:

$15 \div 3 = 5$ We read the question as '15 divided by 3'.

$$3\overline{)15} = 5$$

We read the question as 'how many 3s are there in 15?'

The questions mean the same.

QUICK TIP!
Line up the **answer** tens and units (above the line) with the tens and units beneath the line.

1. **Carefully write these division number sentences in another way.**

$$7\overline{)21} = 3$$

a $21 \div 7 = 3$ b $30 \div 6 = 5$

c $12 \div 3 = 4$ d $24 \div 4 = 6$

e $40 \div 5 = 8$ f $28 \div 4 = 7$

g $50 \div 10 = 5$ h $27 \div 3 = 9$

2. **Work out the answers to these questions.**

a $3\overline{)18} = 6$ b $5\overline{)25}$ c $4\overline{)20}$

d $3\overline{)30}$ e $2\overline{)18}$ f $10\overline{)90}$

g $2\overline{)16}$ h $5\overline{)35}$ i $5\overline{)30}$

No Nonsense
Maths

8-9 years

Parents' notes

What your child will learn from this book

Bond No Nonsense will help your child to understand and become more confident in their maths work. This book features all the main maths objectives covered by your child's class teacher during the school year. It provides clear, straightforward teaching and learning of the essentials in a rigorous, step-by-step way.

How you can help

Following a few simple guidelines will ensure that your child gets the best from this book:

- Explain that the book will help your child become confident in their maths work.
- If your child has difficulty reading the text on the page or understanding a question, do provide help.
- Provide scrap paper to give your child extra space for rough working.
- Encourage your child to complete all the exercises in a lesson. You can mark the work using this answer section (which you will also find on the website). Your child can record their own impressions of the work using the 'How did I do' feature.

0			19
	Tough	OK	Got it!

- The 'How am I doing?' sections provide a further review of progress.

Using the website – www.bondlearning.co.uk

- The website provides extra practice of every skill in the book. So if your child does not feel confident about a lesson, they can go to the website and have another go.
- For every page of this book you will find further practice questions and their answers available to download.
- To access the extra practice pages:
  1. Go to www.bondlearning.co.uk
  2. Click on 'Maths'.
  3. Click on '8-9 years'.
  4. Click on the lesson you want.

Bond No Nonsense 8-9 years Answers

(1) Thousands, hundreds, tens and units pp2–3
1. **b** 7450   **c** 1001   **d** 3911   **e** 7652   **f** 9999
2. **b** 600   **c** 70   **d** 5   **e** 2000   **f** 2
3. **a** One thousand, two hundred and seventy-six
   b Five thousand, six hundred and twenty-eight
   c Four thousand, six hundred
   d Two thousand, eight hundred and ninety
4. 1796 1976 3218 3812
5. **a** 7281   **b** 5820   **c** 3985   **d** 4796   **e** 9671   **f** 7772

Challenge yourself
a 2379   **b** 9732
c Two thousand, seven hundred and ninety-three

(2) Addition pp4–5
1. **a** 171   **b** 281   **c** 296   **d** 461   **e** 382   **f** 391
2. **a** 291   **b** 380   **c** 452   **d** 272   **e** 345   **f** 410

Challenge yourself

25	25	25	68	68	68	17	17	42
+68	+17	+79	+17	+42	+79	+42	+79	+79
93	42	104	85	110	147	59	96	121

(3) Subtraction pp6–7
1. **a** 29   **b** 57   **c** 28   **d** 66   **e** 9   **f** 17   **g** 25   **h** 27

Challenge yourself
Answers will vary

(4) 3 and 4 times tables pp8–9
1. 3 6 9 12 15 18 21 24 27 30
   4 8 12 16 20 24 28 32 36 40
2. **a** 12 (15) 18 21 (24) 27 30 33
   b (20) 24 28 32 (36) 40 44 48
3. **a** 12   **b** 40   **c** 24   **d** 21   **e** 36   **f** 24
4. **a** 9   **b** 32   **c** 21   **d** 30   **e** 16   **f** 8   **g** 27   **h** 36

Challenge yourself
a 3   **b** 3   **c** 6   **d** 9   **e** 4   **f** 9   **g** 8   **h** 10
i 4   **j** 3

(5) Division facts pp10–11
1. **b** 4   **c** 3   **d** 4   **e** 4 × 4   **f** 5 × 4   **g** 6 × 5
   h 30 = (3 × 10)
2. **a** 5   **b** 4   **c** 8   **d** 7 7   **e** 8 8   **f** 5 5
3. **a** 4   **b** 5   **c** 9   **d** 9   **e** 3   **f** 10

Challenge yourself
a 5   **b** 10

(6) Multiplying and dividing by 10 pp12–13
1. **a** 10   **b** 20   **c** 30   **d** 40   **e** 50   **f** 60
2. **b** 370   **c** 580   **d** 960   **e** 1210   **f** 1130
3. 8 600   2 900
   86 000   29 000
4. **a** 1   **b** 4   **c** 2   **d** 5   **e** 3   **f** 6
5. **b** 8   **c** 12   **d** 17   **e** 15   **f** 19   **g** 22   **h** 36

Challenge yourself
a £1·40 or 140p   **b** 42p   **c** 26

(7) Fractions pp14–15
1. **b** $\frac{2}{8}$ **c** $\frac{4}{10}$ **d** $\frac{2}{6}$
2. $\frac{3}{4}$ $\frac{2}{3}$ $\frac{7}{8}$ $\frac{6}{10}$
3. **a** $\frac{2}{2}$ **b** $\frac{10}{10}$ **c** $\frac{3}{3}$
4. **b** $\frac{2}{3}$ **c** $\frac{4}{5}$

Challenge yourself

$\frac{4}{8}$	$\frac{1}{2}$
$\frac{2}{10}$	$\frac{1}{5}$
$\frac{2}{2}$	$\frac{7}{7}$
$\frac{2}{3}$	$\frac{4}{6}$
$\frac{6}{8}$	$\frac{3}{4}$

(8) Money pp16–17
1. **a** £3·87   **b** 13p   **c** £2·99   **d** £1·09   **e** £6·22
   f £1·19   **g** £8·21   **h** £0·67 or 67p   **i** £9·68
2. **b** 520p   **c** 1088p   **d** 2809p
3. **b** £2·50   **c** £8·93   **d** £31·64
4. **a** Yes   **b** £7·79   **c** £2·21

Challenge yourself

	a			b	
	16p	£1·00		£4·78	£20·00
	× 5	− 0·80		× 3	− £14·34
	80p	20p		£14·34	£ 5·66

	c			
	50p	20p	£1·00	£1·40 (total money Brian has)
	+ 50p	+20p	+ 40p	−£0·90 (cost of the ride)
	£1·00	40p	£1·40	£0·50 (money left)

(9) Time – analogue and digital pp18–19
1. **b** 10:35   **c** 2:05   **d** 6:45   **e** 1:20   **f** 3:55
2. **a**

d   **e**   **f**

Challenge yourself
a 60   **b** 60   **c** 24   **d** 7   **e** 52   **f** 100

(10) Co-ordinates pp20–21
1. **a** (4, 2)   **b** (1, 3)   **c** (3, 2)   **d** (5, 1)
2.

a fish

Challenge yourself
Answers will vary

How am I doing? pp22–23
1. 1796 2138 2238 3926
2. **a** 182   **b** 161   **c** 261   **d** 203
3. **a** 48   **b** 29   **c** 28   **d** 32
4. **a** 12   **b** 36   **c** 24   **d** 30   **e** 24   **f** 9
5. **a** 3 and 3   **b** 3 and 3   **c** 2 and 2   **d** 5 and 5
6. **a** 210   **b** 36   **c** 390   **d** 11   **e** 550   **f** 28
7. **a** 1   **b** $\frac{2}{3}$ **c** $\frac{5}{10}$ **d** $\frac{3}{5}$

8. a £4·51   **b** £2·30   **c** £7·73   **d** £8·06

9. a 4:35   **b** 2:55

10. a
b

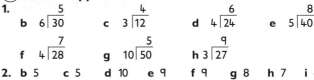

⑪ Greater than, less than pp24–25

1. a 4582   **b** 1197   **c** 421 m   **d** 1019 m   **e** 863 g
   f 5218 kg

2. a 7361   6371   3671   1763   1367
   b 5534   5435   5345   4553   3455
   c 9281   8921   8129   1928   1298

3. a Answers will vary   **b** Answers will vary
   c Answers will vary   **d** Answers will vary

4. a <   **b** >   **c** >   **d** <   **e** <   **f** >   **g** >   **h** >

Challenge yourself

a Any number greater than 470
b Any number smaller than 699
c A number between 1450 and 3280
d A number between 458 and 500
e A number less than 500
f A number greater than 7333

⑫ Negative numbers pp26–27

1. a −1°C   **b** −5°C   **c** 1°C   **d** −7°C   **e** 8°C   **f** −3°C

2. (approximate answers)
   a −2   **b** 8   **c** −5   **d** 3   **e** −7   **f** −1

3. | -11 | -10 | -9 | -8 | -7 | -6 | -5 | -4 | -3 | -2 | -1 | 0 | 1 | 2 | 3 | 4 | 5 |

Challenge yourself

⑬ Number sequences pp28–29

1. b 20   15   10   5   down 5
   c 30   28   26   24   down 2
   d 19   16   13   10   down 3

2. a 27   47   52   67   **b** 87   83   79   75
   c 26   38   50   62   **d** 63   54   51   48

3. a 12   6   −2   **b** −4   5   14   23
   c 45   20   15   0   **d** −5   3   27   35

Challenge yourself

4, 8, 12, 16, 20, 24, 28, 32, 36 should be coloured.
Reference should be made to the pattern of the coloured squares.
44 – Yes   53 – No

⑭ Multiplication 1 pp30–31

1. a 60
         24

   b 50
          45

   c 60
           3

   d 60
          30
         ____
          90

   e 40
           6
         ____
          46

   f 40
          16
         ____
          56

2. a 50
          45
         ____
          95

   b 20
           6
         ____
          26

   c 30
          21
         ____
          51

   d 90
           9
         ____
          99

   e 80
          40
         ____
         120

   f 50
          30
         ____
          80

Challenge yourself

a 75   **b** 70   **c** 145

⑮ Division pp32–33

1. b 6)30 = 5   **c** 3)12 = 4   **d** 4)24 = 6   **e** 5)40 = 8
   f 4)28 = 7   **g** 10)50 = 5   **h** 3)27 = 9

2. b 5   **c** 5   **d** 10   **e** 9   **f** 9   **g** 8   **h** 7   **i** 6

3. a 24   **b** 19   **c** 23   **d** 24   **e** 15   **f** 27

Challenge yourself
a 19   **b** 16

⑯ 6 times table pp34–35

1. 6   12   18   24   30   36   42   48   54   60

2. a | 6 | 12 | **18** | 24 | **30** | 36 | **42** | 48 |
   b | **18** | 24 | 30 | **36** | **42** | **48** | **54** | **60** |
   c | 6 | **12** | **18** | 24 | **30** | **36** | **42** | 48 |

3. a 48   **b** 24   **c** 42   **d** 54   **e** 12   **f** 18

4. a 24   **b** 54   **c** 12   **d** 30   **e** 18   **f** 36   **g** 60   **h** 48

Challenge yourself

a 6   **b** 60   **c** 1   **d** 3   **e** 7   **f** 6
g Any number   **h** 8

⑰ Polygons pp36–37

1. a 4 (a, c, e and f)   **b** a, c
   c 0   **d** 5 (all except e)

2. Answers will vary

3. b (irregular) hexagon   **c** (irregular) pentagon
   d (regular) octagon   **e** rectangle
   f (irregular) heptagon

4. Answers will vary

Challenge yourself

a quadrilateral   **b** equilateral   **c** hexagons
d isosceles   **e** heptagons

⑱ Perimeter pp38–39

1. b 3 + 3 + 3 = 9 cm
   c 6 + 5 + 6 + 5 = 22 cm   = (2 × 6) + (2 × 5) = 22 cm
   d 8 + 4 + 8 + 4 = 24 cm   = (2 × 8) + (2 × 4) = 24 cm

2. a 18 cm   **b** 20 cm   **c** 16 cm   **d** 40 cm

Challenge yourself

a 7 cm
b Any one of: 7 cm × 7 cm, 8 cm × 6 cm, 10 cm × 4 cm, 11 cm × 3 cm, 12 cm × 2 cm, 13 cm × 1 cm

⑲ Bar Charts pp40–41

1. a yellow   **b** red, blue   **c** green   **d** 125

2.

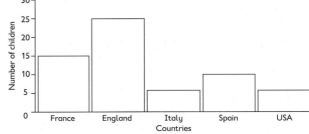

Challenge yourself

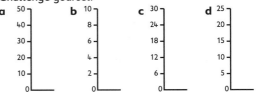

How am I doing? pp42–43

1. a >   **b** >   **c** >   **d** <   **e** <   **f** >

2. a −4°C   **b** −8°C

3. a 60   64   68   72   76   **b** 26   21   16   11   6

A3

4. a 50
30
─────
80

b 30 (10 × 3)
24 (8 × 3)
─────
54

c 60 (10 × 6)
12 (2 × 6)
─────
72

5. a 48   **b** 16   **c** 25   **d** 17
6. a 18   **b** 54   **c** 60   **d** 24   **e** 48   **f** 36
7. Regular pentagon (size may vary)
8. a 10 cm = (2 × 2) + (3 × 2) = 4 + 6 = 10 cm
b 20 cm = 5 × 4 = 20 cm

⑳ **Rounding numbers pp44–45**
1. b 360   **c** 680   **d** 810   **e** 560   **f** 500
2. a 300   **b** 700   **c** 400   **d** 800   **e** 300   **f** 900
3. a 520   **b** 700   **c** 300   **d** 330
4. Answers can include the numbers stated.
a A number between 145 and 149
b A number between 701 and 749
c A number between 871 and 874
d A number between 405 and 409

Challenge yourself
b 57 + 91   60 + 90
c 65 + 23   70 + 20
d 17 + 99   20 + 100
e 38 + 46   40 + 50

㉑ **Multiplication 2 pp46–47**
1. a 80 (10 × 8)
16 (2 × 8)
─────
96

b 20 (10 × 2)
14 (7 × 2)
─────
34

c 50 (10 × 5)
25 (5 × 5)
─────
75

d 40 (10 × 4)
12 (3 × 4)
─────
52

e 80 (20 × 4)
4 (1 × 4)
─────
84

f 30 (10 × 3)
24 (8 × 3)
─────
54

g 60 (10 × 6)
30 (5 × 6)
─────
90

h 60 (10 × 6)
36 (6 × 6)
─────
96

i 60 (30 × 2)
8 (4 × 2)
─────
68

2. a 72   **b** 72
3. a 40 + 6 = 46
b 60 + 18 = 78
c 1200 + 100 + 0 = 1300
d 2000 + 1400 + 0 + 0 = 3400
e 80 + 8 = 88
f 4000 + 800 + 100 + 0 = 4900

Challenge yourself
a 88   **b** 72   **c** 104

㉒ **7 times table pp48–49**
1. 7 14 21 28 35 42 49 56 63 70

2. a | 7 | 14 | **21** | **28** | 35 | **42** | **49** | 56 |

b | 7 | 14 | **21** | **28** | **35** | **42** | 49 | 56 |

c | **21** | **28** | 35 | **42** | **49** | 56 | **63** | 70 |

3. a 42   **b** 28   **c** 63   **d** 0   **e** 21   **f** 70
4. a 28   **b** 63   **c** 35   **d** 21   **e** 42   **f** 56   **g** 14   **h** 49

Challenge yourself
a 3   **b** 7   **c** 35   **d** 2   **e** 8   **f** 4   **g** 0   **h** 7

㉓ **Decimals pp50–51**
1. a 0·4   **b** 0·8   **c** 0·3   **d** 0·6   **e** 0·1   **f** 0·9
2. a 0·5 0·6 0·7 0·8 0·9 1·2 1·3 1·4
b 3·5 3·2 2·8 2·6 2·5 2·4

3.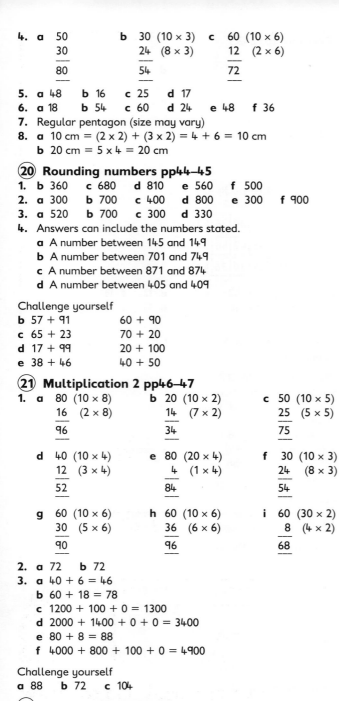

4. a 0·5   **b** 0·7   **c** 0·1   **d** 0·2

Challenge yourself
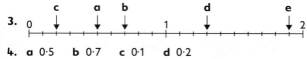
1.2 1.6 2.1 2.8 3.0 4.5

A4

㉔ **Estimation pp52–53**
1. All answers approximate:
a 60   **b** 90   **c** 25   **d** 800   **e** 35   **f** 150

2. a b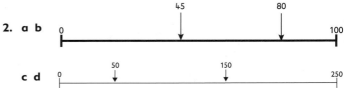
c d
3. a 200 (approximate answer)
b There are just under half of the sweets left.

Challenge yourself
a Answers will vary   **b** Answers will vary

㉕ **Solving problems pp54–55**
1. a 6 (1 + 2 + 3)   **b** 9 (2 + 3 + 4)
12 (3 + 4 + 5)   15 (4 + 5 + 6)
c The totals are 3 times the middle number.
d The middle number of the sequence.
e 12 + 13 + 14 (39 ÷ 3 = 13 to get middle number in sequence)
2. a 5 and 3   **b** 9 and 3   **c** 6 and 6   **d** 11 and 2

Challenge yourself
a 120 g earth, 50 g green grass and 50 ml of puddle water
b 100 ml   **c** 480 g

㉖ **Line symmetry pp56–57**
1. a   **b**   **c**

2. b   **c**   **d**   **e**   **f**

3. b   **c**   **d**

Challenge yourself
Inside circle any of: square, rectangle, rhombus, kite, arrowhead, isosceles trapezium.
Outsite circle any of: prallelogram, other irregular quadrilaterals.

㉗ **Area pp58–59**
1. a 11 cm²   **b** 13 cm²   **c** 8 cm²   **d** 7 cm²
2. Answers will vary
3. a 10 cm²   **b** 12 cm²

Challenge yourself
Answers will vary

㉘ **Length, mass, capacity pp60–61**
1. a millimetre, centimetre, metre, kilometre (any 3 from 4)
b litre, millilitre
c gram, kilogram
2. a 500 ml   **b** 5 mm   **c** 500 g   **d** 500 m   **e** 50 cm
f 25 cm   **g** 250 ml   **h** 250 g
3. a 2 kg   **b** 50 mm   **c** 3000 ml   **d** 2.5 m
e 7,000,000 m   **f** 230 mm   **g** 1.5 kg   **h** 500 mm

Challenge yourself
a metres   **b** kilometres   **c** grams   **d** litres
e Answers will vary   **f** Answers will vary
g Answers will vary   **h** Answers will vary

How am I doing? pp62–63
1. a 570   **b** 600   **c** 240   **d** 200
2. a 44   **b** 70   **c** 112   **d** 122
3. a 35   **b** 63   **c** 42   **d** 14   **e** 49   **f** 56

4. a 0 — 1 (1·4) 2   **b** 0 — 1 (1·7) 2

5. a 60   **b** 150 (approximate answers)

6. a   **b**   **c**

7. a 13 cm²   **b** 2 cm²   **c** 12 cm²
8. a 1 metre or 1 m   **b** 3 litres or 3 l   **c** 5000 grams or 5000 g

We divide larger numbers like this:

85 ÷ 5   5⟌85

First we ask how many 5s in 8:   **1**
(8 ÷ 5 = 1 r3)   5⟌8 ³5

(We carry the 3 to the next column.)

Now we ask how many 5s in 35:   1 **7**
(35 ÷ 5 = 7)   5⟌8 ³5

---

3. Divide the following.

a 2⟌48   **b** 5⟌95   **c** 3⟌69

d 4⟌96   **e** 5⟌75   **f** 3⟌81

0		21
Tough	OK	Got it!

Total

21

More practice? Go to

Challenge yourself

Work out the answers to these problems.

a A balloon race had been organised at Crudwell Village fete.
76 balloons were released. An equal number of red, yellow, green and
blue balloons were used.
How many green balloons were released? _____

b Jacob, Wusai and Reece were collecting conkers.
They collected a total of 48 conkers which they split equally between them.
How many conkers did they each have? _____

6 times table

7 lots of 6 is 42.

$$6 + 6 + 6 + 6 + 6 + 6 + 6 \quad = 42$$

$$7 \times 6 = 42$$

1. **Complete the 6 times table.**

$1 \times 6 =$ _____ $6 \times 6 =$ _____

$2 \times 6 =$ _____ $7 \times 6 =$ _____

$3 \times 6 =$ _____ $8 \times 6 =$ _____

$4 \times 6 =$ _____ $9 \times 6 =$ _____

$5 \times 6 =$ _____ $10 \times 6 =$ _____

2. **Finish the 6 times table number sequences.**

a
6	12		24		36		48

b
	24	30			48	54	

c
6							48

3. Find the answers.

   a Multiply six by eight. _____

   b What is 4 times 6? _____

   c What are seven sixes? _____

   d Find the answer to nine sixes. _____

   e What is six multiplied by two? _____

   f What is three times six? _____

4. Answer these as quickly as possible.

   a $4 \times 6 =$ _____   **b** $9 \times 6 =$ _____

   c $2 \times 6 =$ _____   **d** $5 \times 6 =$ _____

   e $3 \times 6 =$ _____   **f** $6 \times 6 =$ _____

   g $10 \times 6 =$ _____   **h** $8 \times 6 =$ _____

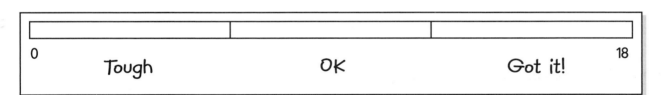

0   Tough   OK   Got it!   18

Total

18

More practice? Go to **www**

Challenge yourself

Fill in the gaps.

   a $6 \times$ _____ $= 36$ **b** $10 \times 6 =$ _____

   c _____ $\times 6 = 6$ **d** _____ $\times 6 = 18$

   e _____ $\times 6 = 42$ **f** $5 \times$ _____ $= 30$

   g $0 \times$ _____ $= 0$ **h** _____ $\times 6 = 48$

Polygons

A **polygon** is any shape with three or more **straight** sides.

All sides and angles of a **regular** polygon are equal.

1. **Look at these polygons and answer the questions.**

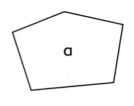 a

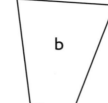 b

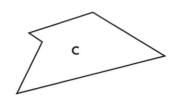 c

 d

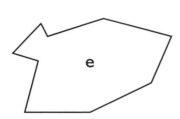 e

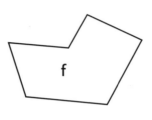 f

a How many polygons have more than four angles? _____

b Which polygons have five sides? _____

c How many of these polygons are regular? _____

d How many polygons have fewer than nine sides? _____

2. **Draw three different irregular polygons of your own with ...**

3 sides	6 sides	4 sides

3. Name each of these polygons.

a

triangle

b

_____

c

_____

d

_____

e

_____

f

_____

4. Draw three regular polygons with ...

3 sides	6 sides	4 sides

0   15

Tough   OK   Got it!

Total

15

More practice? Go to www

Challenge yourself

Fill in the correct word to complete each description.

hexagons   isosceles   heptagons   quadrilateral   equilateral

a   A _____ is any shape with four straight sides.

b   An _____ triangle is an example of a regular polygon.

c   All shapes with six sides are _____.

d   An _____ triangle is an example of a irregular polygon.

e   All _____ have seven sides.

Perimeter

Follow the edge of this rectangle with your pencil.

You have just drawn around the **perimeter** of this shape.

A **perimeter** is the outside edge of a shape.
Look at how we find the perimeter of a shape.

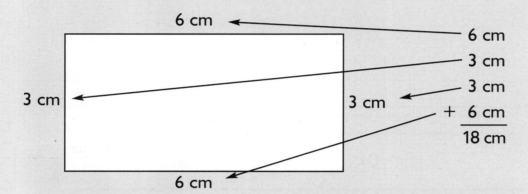

3 cm + 3 cm + 6 cm + 6 cm = 18 cm **or** (2 × 3 cm) + (2 × 6 cm) = 18 cm

The perimeter is **18 cm**.

1. **Find the perimeter of these shapes.**

a
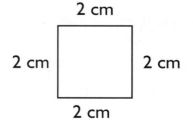

b
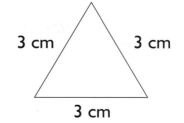

= __2__ cm + __2__ cm + __2__ cm + __2__ cm   = _____ cm + _____ cm + _____ cm

= __8__ cm   = _____ cm

c

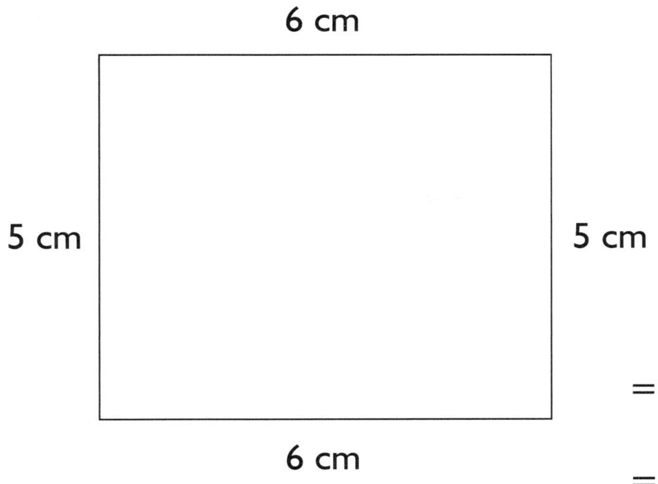

6 cm

5 cm   5 cm

6 cm

= ____ + ____ + ____ + ____ = ____ cm

= (2 × ____) + (2 × ____) = ____ cm

d

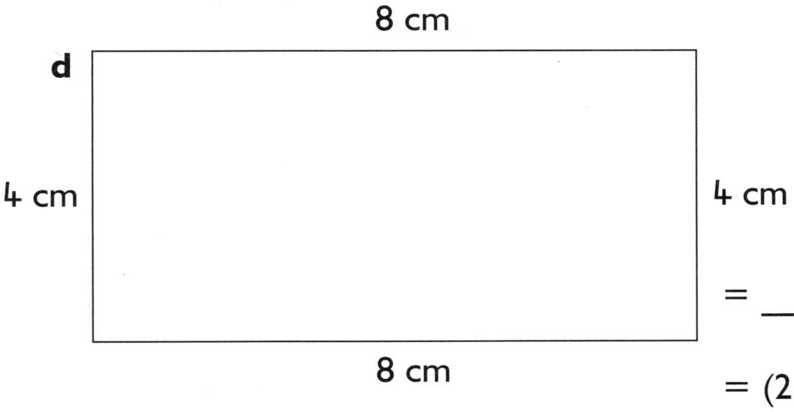

8 cm

4 cm   4 cm

8 cm

= ____ + ____ + ____ + ____ = ____ cm

= (2 × ____) + (2 × ____) = ____ cm

2. **Find the perimeter of a...**

a   5 cm × 4 cm rectangle. _____

b   7 cm × 3 cm rectangle. _____

c   4 cm × 4 cm square. _____

d   10 cm × 10 cm square. _____

| 0 | Tough | OK | Got it! | 7 |

Total

7

More practice? Go to www

Challenge yourself

a   The perimeter of a square is 28 cm. How many cm is one side? _____

b   Now draw a rectangle with the same perimeter as the square (28 cm).

Bar charts

A **bar chart** shows information in a simple way.
A bar chart should always have a title and labels on the axes.

This bar chart shows information about a large number of children. To keep the bar chart a sensible size, each interval shows 5 children.

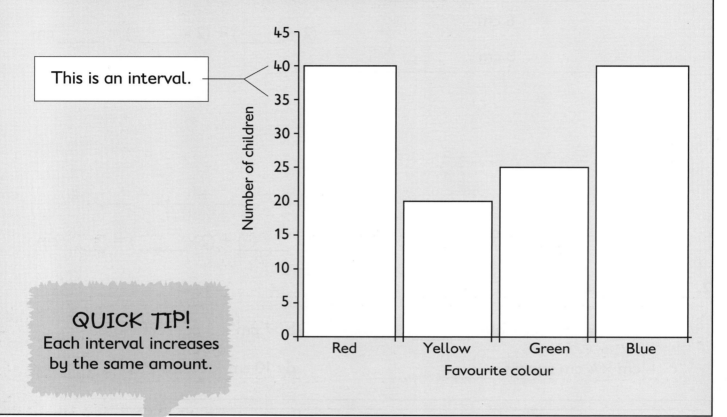

This is an interval.

QUICK TIP!
Each interval increases by the same amount.

1. **Look carefully at the information the bar chart gives, and answer the questions.**

   a Which colour is the least popular? _____

   b Which colours are the most popular? _____

   c Which colour is liked by 15 fewer children than those who like blue? _____

   d How many children altogether were surveyed? _____

2. **Draw the information below on the bar chart.**

60 children were asked where they went on holiday last year.

Countries	Number of children
France	15
England	25
Italy	5
Spain	10
USA	5

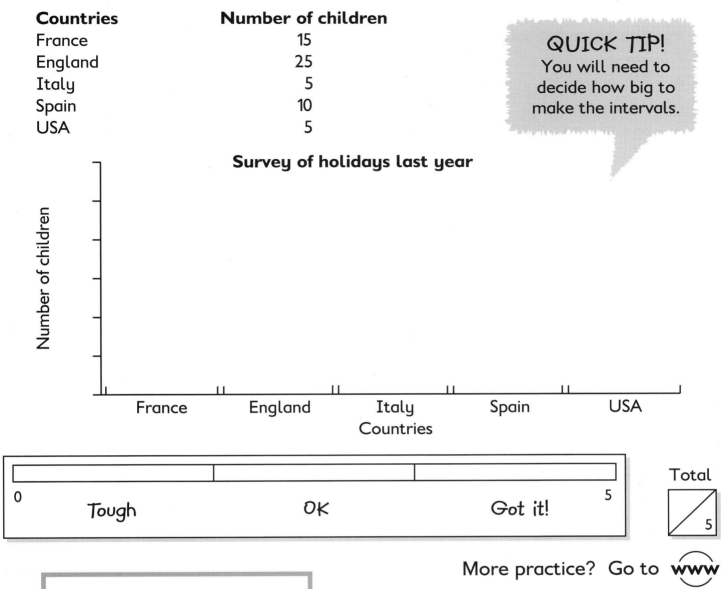

Survey of holidays last year

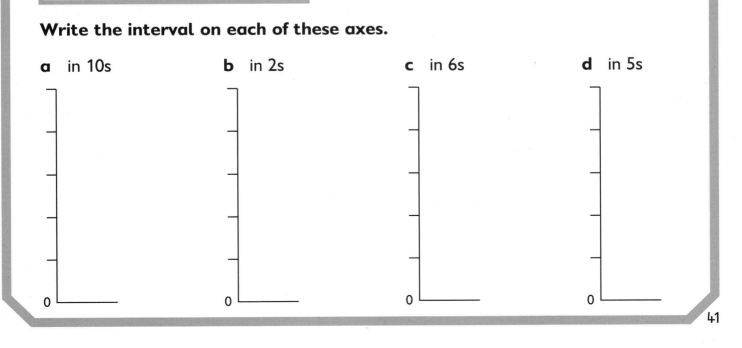

			Total
0		5	
Tough	OK	Got it!	/ 5

More practice? Go to www

Challenge yourself

Write the interval on each of these axes.

a in 10s   **b** in 2s   **c** in 6s   **d** in 5s

How am I doing?

1. **Put the correct > or < sign in each box.**

    a 56 ☐ 54   **b** 87 ☐ 23

    c 90 ☐ 82   **d** 34 ☐ 43

    e 245 ☐ 254   **f** 396 ☐ 369

2. **What is the temperature on these thermometers?**

    a   **b**

    _____ °C   _____ °C

3. **Look at the number sequences. Which numbers come next?**

a

32	36	40	44	48	52	56					

b

61	56	51	46	41	36	31					

4. **Complete the following:**

    a   16   **b**   18   **c**   12

       ×   5   ×   3   ×   6

                (10×5)

                (6×5)

                (16×5)

5. **Work out the answers.**

a $2\overline{)96}$ b $4\overline{)64}$

c $3\overline{)75}$ d $5\overline{)85}$

6. **Answer these as quickly as you can.**

a $3 \times 6 =$ _____   b $9 \times 6 =$ _____

c $10 \times 6 =$ _____   d $4 \times 6 =$ _____

e $8 \times 6 =$ _____   f $6 \times 6 =$ _____

7. **Draw a regular polygon with 5 sides.**

8. **Find the perimeter of a ...**

a $2 \text{ cm} \times 3 \text{ cm}$ rectangle. _____

b $5 \text{ cm} \times 5 \text{ cm}$ square. _____

Total

26

More practice? Go to

Rounding numbers

Look at the number line.

450   457   460

457 is closer to 460 than 450.

We say the nearest ten to 457 is 460 **or**
457 **rounded to the nearest ten** is 460.

QUICK TIP!
Remember, when the number is halfway between two numbers we round **up**.

1. **Complete the following sentences.**

a 421 rounded to the nearest ten is ___420___.

b 356 rounded to the nearest ten is _____.

c 675 rounded to the nearest ten is _____.

d 812 rounded to the nearest ten is _____.

e 555 rounded to the nearest ten is _____.

f 498 rounded to the nearest ten is _____.

Now we are going to **round to the nearest hundred**.
We do this in the same way but this time round to the nearest hundred.

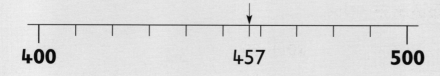

400   457   500

457 is closer to 500 than 400.
We say the nearest hundred to 457 is 500 **or**
457 **rounded to the nearest hundred** is 500.

2. Complete the following sentences.

a 321 rounded to the nearest hundred is _____.

b 689 rounded to the nearest hundred is _____.

c 443 rounded to the nearest hundred is _____.

d 750 rounded to the nearest hundred is _____.

e 302 rounded to the nearest hundred is _____.

f 949 rounded to the nearest hundred is _____.

3. Fill in the gaps.

a 521 is closer to _____ than 530.

b 709 rounded to the nearest hundred is _____.

c 278 is closer to _____ than 200.

d 333 rounded to the nearest ten is _____.

4. Write a number that is nearer to...

a ...150 than 140. _____

b ...700 than 800. _____

c ...870 than 880. _____

d ...410 than 400. _____

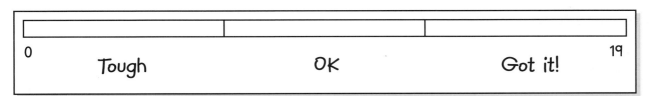

0   Tough   OK   Got it!   19

Total

19

More practice? Go to www

Challenge yourself

Join with a line the best approximation.

a	34 + 29	40 + 50
b	57 + 91	70 + 20
c	65 + 23	30 + 30
d	17 + 99	60 + 90
e	38 + 46	20 + 100

45

Multiplication 2

Do you remember how to multiply large numbers?

$$
\begin{array}{r}
15 \\
\times\ 7 \\
\hline
70 \\
35 \\
\hline
105 \\
\hline
\end{array}
\quad
\begin{array}{l}
(10 \times 7) \\
(\ 5 \times 7) \\
(15 \times 7)
\end{array}
$$

If you have forgotten, don't worry. Turn back to page 30 to refresh your memory.

1.   Find the answers.

a $\begin{array}{r} 12 \\ \times\ 8 \\ \hline \\ \hline \end{array}$

b $\begin{array}{r} 17 \\ \times\ 2 \\ \hline \\ \hline \end{array}$

c $\begin{array}{r} 15 \\ \times\ 5 \\ \hline \\ \hline \end{array}$

d $\begin{array}{r} 13 \\ \times\ 4 \\ \hline \\ \hline \end{array}$

e $\begin{array}{r} 21 \\ \times\ 4 \\ \hline \\ \hline \end{array}$

f $\begin{array}{r} 18 \\ \times\ 3 \\ \hline \\ \hline \end{array}$

g $\begin{array}{r} 15 \\ \times\ 6 \\ \hline \\ \hline \end{array}$

h $\begin{array}{r} 16 \\ \times\ 6 \\ \hline \\ \hline \end{array}$

i $\begin{array}{r} 34 \\ \times\ 2 \\ \hline \\ \hline \end{array}$

2. **Solve these problems.**

   a Mum and Dad handed out 4 bags of sweets.
   In each bag there were 18 sweets.
   How many sweets were there altogether?

   _____

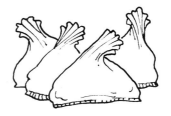

   b Mrs Gallop bought 6 packs of pencils for her class.
   There were 12 pencils in each pack.
   How many pencils did she buy altogether?

   _____

Doubling numbers can help us calculate some multiplication problems.

Double 46 is ...double 40 + double 6

$$80 \quad + \quad 12 \quad = 92$$

---

3. **What is...**

For your workings

   a double 23? _____   **b** double 39? _____

   c double 650? _____   **d** double 1700? _____

   e double 44? _____   **f** double 2450? _____

0			17
Tough	OK	Got it!	

Total

/17

More practice? Go to

Challenge yourself

   a If $1 \times 22 = 22$ and $2 \times 22 = 44$, what does 4×22 equal? _____

   b If $1 \times 18 = 18$ and $2 \times 18 = 36$, what does 4×18 equal? _____

   c If $2 \times 13 = 26$ and $4 \times 13 = 52$, what does 8×13 equal? _____

7 times table

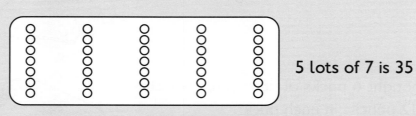

5 lots of 7 is 35

7 + 7 + 7 + 7 + 7 = 35

5 x 7 = 35

1. Complete the 7 times table.

$1 \times 7 =$ _____ $6 \times 7 =$ _____

$2 \times 7 =$ _____ $7 \times 7 =$ _____

$3 \times 7 =$ _____ $8 \times 7 =$ _____

$4 \times 7 =$ _____ $9 \times 7 =$ _____

$5 \times 7 =$ _____ $10 \times 7 =$ _____

2. Finish the 7 times table number sequences.

a

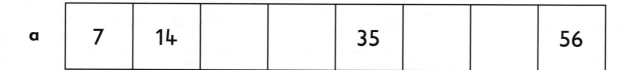

| 7 | 14 | | | 35 | | | 56 |

b

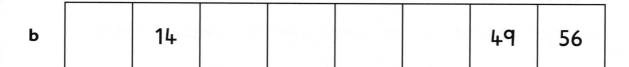

| | 14 | | | | | 49 | 56 |

c

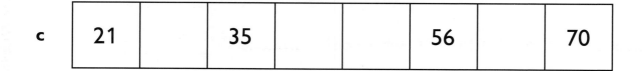

| 21 | | 35 | | | 56 | | 70 |

3. **What is....**

a six multiplied by seven? _____

b 4 times 7? _____

c seven nines? _____

d seven multiplied by zero? _____

e 7 multiplied by 3? _____

f ten times seven? _____

4. **Answer these as quickly as possible.**

a $4 \times 7 =$ _____   **b** $7 \times 9 =$ _____

c $5 \times 7 =$ _____   **d** $7 \times 3 =$ _____

e $7 \times 6 =$ _____   **f** $7 \times 8 =$ _____

g $2 \times 7 =$ _____   **h** $7 \times 7 =$ _____

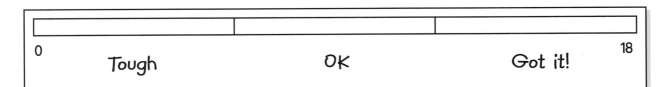

0			18
Tough	OK	Got it!	

Total

18

More practice? Go to www

Challenge yourself

Fill in the gaps.

a _____ $\times 7 = 21$ **b** $10 \times$ _____ $= 70$

c $5 \times 7 =$ _____   **d** _____ $\times 7 = 14$

e _____ $\times 7 = 56$ **f** _____ $\times 7 = 28$

g _____ $\times 7 = 0$ **h** $7 \times$ _____ $= 49$

Decimals

Decimals are a type of fraction, sometimes called **decimal fractions**. Look at this number line. It shows decimal fractions.

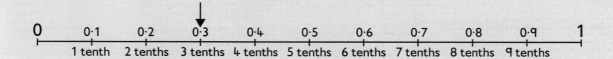

| 0 | 0·1 | 0·2 | 0·3 | 0·4 | 0·5 | 0·6 | 0·7 | 0·8 | 0·9 | 1 |
| | 1 tenth | 2 tenths | 3 tenths | 4 tenths | 5 tenths | 6 tenths | 7 tenths | 8 tenths | 9 tenths | |

The space between each whole number is split into 10 smaller parts called **tenths**.

Look at the arrow. It is pointing at 0·3.

That means 3 tenths.

The · in between the numbers is called a **decimal point**.

1. **Look at the number lines and write the decimal to which the arrow is pointing.**

a
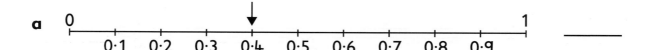
_____

b

_____

c
_____

d
_____

e

_____

f

_____

2. Finish these number lines.

a

0·1	0·2	0·3	0·4						1·0	1·1				1·5

b

3·7	3·6		3·4	3·3		3·1	3·0	2·9		2·7				2·3

3. **Draw and label arrows on the number line to mark the decimals.**

  a 0·5   **b** 0·7   **c** 0·2   **d** 1·3   **e** 1·9

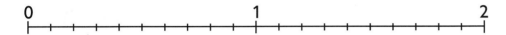

4. **Look at the number line.**
Write the decimal each fraction is equivalent to.

QUICK TIP!
'Equivalent to' means
'has the same value as'

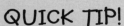

a $\dfrac{1}{2} =$ _____   **b** $\dfrac{7}{10} =$ _____   **c** $\dfrac{1}{10} =$ _____   **d** $\dfrac{2}{10} =$ _____

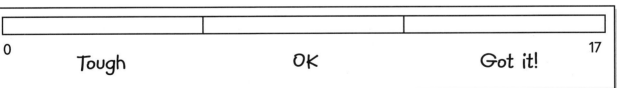

Total

17 / 17

More practice? Go to

Challenge yourself

Look carefully at these numbers.

Write them in order, smallest first.

2·1   1·6   1·2   3·0   4·5   2·8

_____   _____   _____   _____   _____   _____

Estimation

Another way of saying 'guess the nearest number' is **estimate** which number is nearest'.

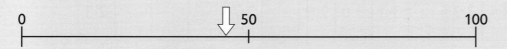

I estimate the arrow is pointing at the number 45.

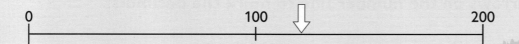

I estimate the arrow is pointing at the number 120.

> **QUICK TIP!**
> Remember to look carefully at the scale of the line.

1. **Estimate which number the arrow is pointing at.**

a Estimation _____

0   50   100

b Estimation _____

0   50   100

c Estimation _____

0   125   250

d Estimation _____

0   500   1000

e Estimation _____

0   100

f Estimation _____

0   250

2. Draw an arrow where you estimate the number will be on the number line.

a 45 0 ⊢————————————————————————————⊣ 100

b 80 0 ⊢————————————————————————————⊣ 100

c 50 0 ⊢————————————————————————————⊣ 250

d 150 0 ⊢————————————————————————————⊣ 250

3. This jar holds **500 sweets** when it is full. Some have been eaten.

a How many are left? _____

b How did you decide?

_____

_____

Tough	OK	Got it!

0   12

Total

12

More practice? Go to **www**

Challenge yourself

Find a book with a page of words.

a Estimate how many words are on the page. _____
(Remember not to count each word.)

b Explain how you made your estimate. _____

_____

Solving problems

Solving problems in maths is a way of playing with numbers.

Approach each problem as a **challenge**!

1. **The consecutive numbers 10, 11 and 12 when added together total 33.**

   a What is the lowest total you can find using

   three consecutive numbers? _____

   QUICK TIP!
   Consecutive numbers
   are numbers that
   follow one after
   another.

   b What is the next lowest total you can find using

   three consecutive numbers? _____

   Do this a number of times.

   c What do you notice about the totals?

   _____

   _____

   d Does the total relate to any of the consecutive numbers you have used each time?

   _____

   e Can you easily find the three consecutive numbers that total 39?

2. The numbers 3 and 7 have a product of 21 and a sum of 10.

Find the two numbers that have...

a a product of 15 and a sum of 8.

b a product of 27 and a sum of 12.

c a product of 36 and a sum of 12.

d a product of 22 and a sum of 13.

0	Tough	OK	Got it!	9

Total

9

More practice? Go to www

Challenge yourself

Do you know how to make mud pies?
This recipe makes one mud pie.

60 g of earth (with all stones removed)
25 g of green grass
25 ml of puddle water

Mix all the ingredients together and then mould the sticky mess into a pie shape.

a Write the total ingredients needed for two mud pies.

_____

_____

_____

b How much puddle water would be needed for four mud pies? _____

c How much earth would be needed for eight mud pies? _____

Line symmetry

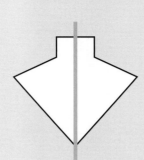 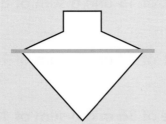

Do you remember?
This is a **line of symmetry**.
It divides a shape into two matching halves.

This is **not** a line of symmetry because the two pieces do not match.

1. **Use a ruler to draw a line of symmetry on each shape.**

    a 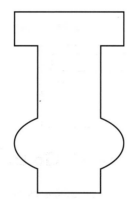   b 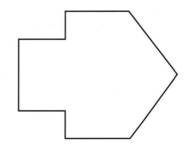   c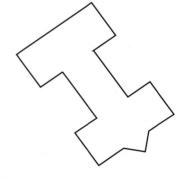

2. **Finish these shapes using the lines of symmetry. Some are quite difficult, so be careful.**

    a 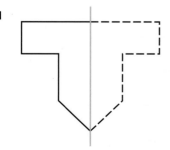   b 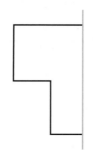   c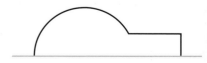

d

e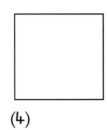

f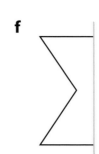

3. **Some shapes have more than one line of symmetry.**
Find all the lines of symmetry on these shapes.

a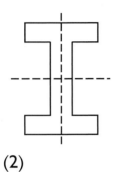

(2)

b

(2)

c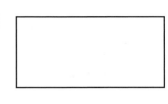

(4)

d

(2)

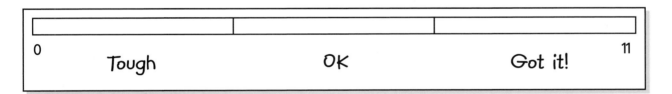

0				11
	Tough	OK	Got it!	

Total

11

More practice? Go to **www**

Challenge yourself

Complete this Venn diagram with six different four-sided shapes.
Three shapes need to be added to each set.

No lines of symmetry

One or more
line of symmetry

Area

Carefully colour the inside of this rectangle green.

You have just coloured in the **area** of this shape.

The **area** is the inside of a shape.
To find the area of a rectangle, draw it on one centimetre squared paper.

Count the number of squares inside the rectangle. There are 15.

The area is 15 cm².

1. **Find the area of these shapes.**

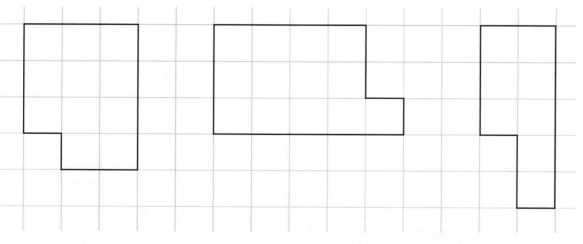

a _____ cm²   b _____ cm²   c _____ cm²

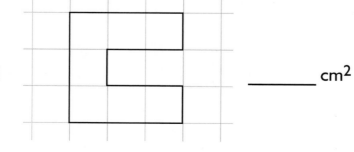

d   _____ cm²

2. Draw shapes with the following areas.

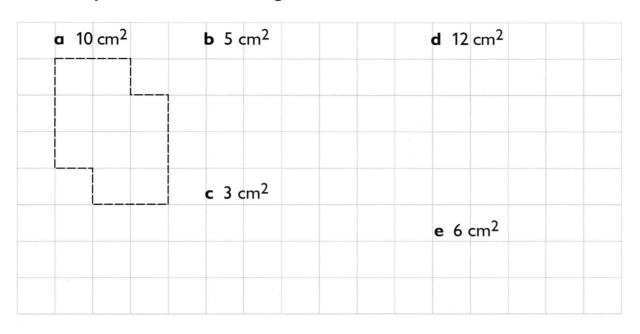

a 10 cm² b 5 cm² d 12 cm²

c 3 cm²

e 6 cm²

3. What is the area of these shapes? Remember you need two $\frac{1}{2}$ squares to equal 1 whole square. ◣ + ◥ = ☐

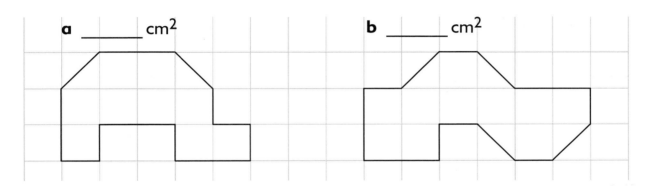

a _____ cm²

b _____ cm²

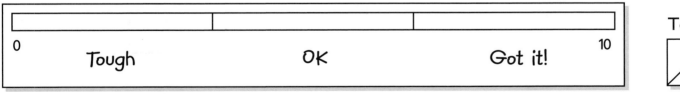

0   Tough   OK   Got it!   10

Total

10

More practice? Go to www

Challenge yourself

Can you find two more ways of halving this 4 x 4 square?

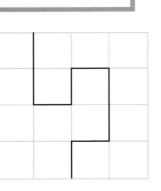
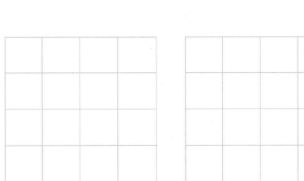

Length, mass, capacity

1 kilometre = 1000 metres
1 metre = 100 centimetres or 1000 millimetres
1 centimetre = 10 millimetres
1 kilogram = 1000 grams
1 litre = 1000 millilitres

1. Answer these questions.

   a List three units of measure we use to measure length.

   _____   _____   _____

   b List two units of measure we use to measure capacity.

   _____   _____

   c List two units of measure we use to measure mass.

   _____   _____

2. What is the equivalent of each of these?

   a $\frac{1}{2}$ of 1 litre = _____ ml   **b** $\frac{1}{2}$ of 1 centimetre = _____ mm

   c $\frac{1}{2}$ of 1 kilogram = _____ g   **d** $\frac{1}{2}$ of 1 kilometre = _____ m

   e $\frac{1}{2}$ of 1 metre = _____ cm   **f** $\frac{1}{4}$ of 1 metre = _____ cm

   g $\frac{1}{4}$ of 1 litre = _____ ml   **h** $\frac{1}{4}$ of 1 kilogram = _____ g

3. **a** Write 2000 g in kilograms. _____

  b Write 5 cm in millimetres. _____

  c Write 3 l in millilitres. _____

  d Write 250 cm in metres. _____

  e Write 7000 km in metres. _____

  f Write 23 cm in millimetres. _____

  g Write 1500 g in kilograms. _____

  h Write 50 cm in millimetres. _____

0 Tough	OK	Got it!	19

Total

19

More practice? Go to www

Challenge yourself

Which metric unit would you use to measure:

a the height of a house? _____

b the distance between London and Hull? _____

c the weight of a shoe? _____

d the capacity of a kettle? _____

Approximately...

e how tall are you? _____

f how far is your school from your house? _____

g how much do you weigh? _____

h how many litres do you drink in a day? _____

How am I doing?

1. **Complete the following sentences.**

    a 569 rounded to the nearest ten is _____.

    b 569 rounded to the nearest hundred is _____.

    c 241 rounded to the nearest ten is _____.

    d 241 rounded to the nearest hundred is _____.

2. **What is...**

    a double 22? _____

    b double 35? _____

    c double 56? _____

    d double 61? _____

3. **Do these as quickly as you can.**

    a $5 \times 7 =$ ___

    b $9 \times 7 =$ ___

    c $6 \times 7 =$ ___

    d $2 \times 7 =$ ___

    e $7 \times 7 =$ ___

    f $8 \times 7 =$ ___

4. **Draw an arrow to mark the decimals on the number line.**

    a 1·4

    0   1   2

    b 1·7

    0   1   2

5. **Estimate which number the arrow is pointing at.**

a Estimation _____

0   ⇩   100

b Estimation _____

0   ⇩   1000

6. **Draw the lines of symmetry on these shapes.**

a   **b**   **c**

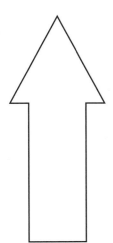      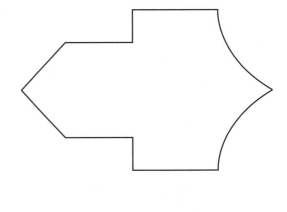

7. **Find the area of these shapes.**

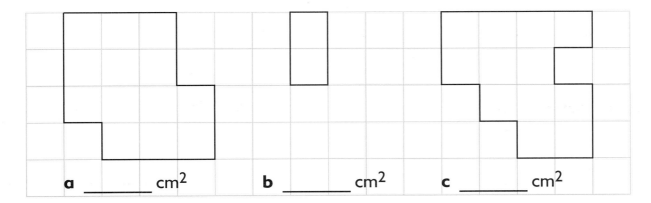

a _____ cm²   **b** _____ cm²   **c** _____ cm²

8. **a** Write 100 cm in metres. _____

    b Write 3000 ml in litres. _____

    c Write 5 kg in grams. _____

Total

/27

More practice? Go to www

Try the 9–10 years book

Lesson 1

Recognising and ordering very big numbers

HUNDRED THOUSAND	TEN THOUSAND	HUNDREDS	THOUSANDS	TENS	UNITS
4	3	7	2	6	9

Four hundred and thirty-seven thousand, two hundred and sixty-nine

1. **Match the written number with the correct card. Join the dots.**

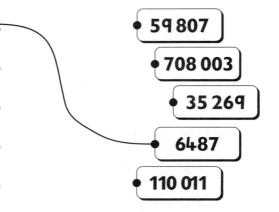

   a Six thousand four hundred and eighty-seven   • 59 807

   b Fifty-nine thousand, eight hundred and seven   • 708 003

   c Thirty-five thousand, two hundred and sixty-nine • 35 269

   d Seven hundred and eight thousand and three   • 6487

   e One hundred and ten thousand and eleven   • 110 011

2. **What number needs to go in the box?**

   a 28 717 = ☐ + 8000 + 700 + 10 + 7

   b 76 923 = 70 000 + ☐ + 900 + 20 + 3

   c 83 641 = 80 000 + 3000 + ☐ + 40 + 1

   d 52 876 = 50 000 + 2000 + 800 + ☐ + 6

   e 39 681 = 30 000 + 9000 + 600 + 80 + ☐

3. **Write these numbers as words.**

   a 7623 _____

   b 223 400 _____

   c 78 231 _____